Dark Chapters: Demo

Legi

© Andrew Smith 2011
First published 2011
ISBN 978 1 84427 623 3

Scripture Union
207–209 Queensway, Bletchley, Milton Keynes, MK2 2EB
Email: info@scriptureunion.org.uk
Website: www.scriptureunion.org.uk

Scripture Union Australia
Locked Bag 2, Central Coast Business Centre, NSW 2252
Website: www.scriptureunion.org.au

Scripture Union USA
PO Box 987, Valley Forge, PA 19482
Website: www.scriptureunion.org

British Library Cataloguing-in-Publication Data
A catalogue record of this book is available from the British Library.

Printed and bound in the UK by Bell and Bain Limited, Glasgow
Cover design: GoBallistic

Scripture Union is an international charity working with churches in more than 130 countries, providing resources to bring the good news of Jesus Christ to children, young people and families and to encourage them to develop spiritually through the Bible and prayer.

As well as our network of volunteers, staff and associates who run holidays, church-based events and school Christian groups, we produce a wide range of publications and support those who use our resources through training programmes.

Legion

The man sat among the tombstones, his ragged clothes hanging off him; in places they were sticking to the blood where he had cut himself. For a moment all was still, though his breathing was heavy and fast. The voices had been tormenting him all night. They hadn't allowed him to sleep properly for months, but for now he could have a few minutes' rest.

He couldn't remember when they had first come to him. It felt as though they had always been there, and he knew it wouldn't be long before they started to scream at him again. When that happened he would do *anything* to try and escape them – he would hit his head, smash his fists against rocks, tear his hair out, anything. Anything to get rid of the voices.

The voices were somewhere inside his head. Lots of them. Sometimes they would just chatter – a constant noise like a waterfall in a cave that drowns out the sounds of the real world. At other times they would laugh and scream like jackals, and at other times they would scream abuse at him, reminding him how evil and worthless he was. But they were always there, like a shadow that can never be removed.

The man looked at the chains hanging off his wrists and tugged half-heartedly at them. That was another attempt by the *normal people* to control him. They would chain him to rocks among the tombs. But the voices would just laugh louder than ever until in desperation he would break the chains that normally no man could break. He was tired. So tired.

The man heard a noise and looked up, exhausted and fearful. It was voices. Voices of *normal people*, and they were coming his way. The voices in his head knew they were coming too and started to chatter and laugh. They made the voices of the *normal people* sound as if they were in another room or even in another dimension. He could see the *normal people* coming towards him. They looked different to the ones who usually came, but it was hard to tell. As the people came nearer and the voices got louder his eyes stopped focusing and everything became distorted. Faces twisted and melted, the ground changed colour and appeared to open up and he could see fire at the bottom of an impossibly deep cavern.

The *normal people* were coming closer, but something was wrong. The voices had started screaming louder than ever before. The screams echoed round his head and seemed to come from the very depths of hell. He tried with all his might to stop them, but the screaming just got louder as the *normal people* approached. As he looked, his eyes distorted the approaching group. They appeared to be stretching and shrinking as they came nearer. But then the man looked again. In the middle of the *normal people* was one man whose shape wasn't changing. Directly he looked at him the voices let forth a scream that seemed to come from the beginning of time and reach across the depths of the universe. His head felt as if it would explode and take the world with it. The voices tried to get him to look away, but something deep within the man's soul was being awakened. Something small and fragile, something that had been buried for years and had been forgotten. Something that the voices wanted to destroy but couldn't – they could only bury it.

That small part of the man forced him to look back to the man whose shape didn't change, who wasn't distorted by the voices. He was standing in front of him now and even appeared to be smiling. The voices were going berserk, the screams drowning out all other sounds. He could see people's lips moving but could make out nothing of what they said. Then he noticed something about the voices. For the first time, they were afraid. It was hardly noticeable at first, but he'd got to know the voices well and fear was definitely there.

Was it this man who was causing their fear? He forced himself once more to look at the man who didn't change shape, and at that moment the voices erupted.

They forced his mouth to work and screamed out across the hills.

'WHAT DO YOU WANT, JESUS, SON OF THE MOST HIGH GOD?'

The man looked at Jesus, and the part of him that was slowly being awakened was being strengthened and beginning to grow. But the voices kept up their constant shrieking, and the fear in the voices carried on growing. Cold fear. Deadly fear.

'Come out,' was all the man, Jesus, said. But to the man it was like a lifeline thrown into an abyss. Those two words cut like a knife through the screams and chatter. He heard them as clearly as if he were free.

'DON'T TORTURE US!' screamed the voices, now in total panic. They seemed to be crawling through his brain trying to find anywhere they could to get away from Jesus.

Once more Jesus spoke, and the man heard his words clearly, like pure water running over a desert.

'What is your name?'

'LEGION,' the voices forced him to shout. In the man's head they were becoming desperate. The man's true identity, which for so long had been crushed, was gaining strength and clarity with every heartbeat. As the voices rushed around his head it was clear they could never escape from Jesus, and in a final desperate act they forced the man to speak one last time.

'SEND US TO THE PIGS.'

Jesus looked and saw a small herd of pigs rummaging among the tombs.

'Go then,' Jesus said. Suddenly the man heard a deafening rushing sound in his head. The voices churned and swirled around inside the man, pulling at every fibre of his body. Then they gave one last blood-curdling cry and flung him to the ground. A great, writhing mass poured out of the man and streaked across the wasteland. The man blinked his eyes and looked up. He saw the face of Jesus smiling at him and holding out his hand. The man paused and looked around. Everything was normal, everything was right. People's faces stayed as they should, the ground was firm and the sunlight made everything look beautiful. It was like waking up on a summer morning after a nightmare that had lasted all night. The man reached out and took Jesus by the hand, and it was then that he noticed. The voices had gone. His head was peaceful. He waited. Still no voices. He was free!

The man started to smile, the first time he'd smiled for years, and then he started to laugh. As he laughed all the other people joined in until the whole place was full of joyful sounds.

All of a sudden the peace was shattered by screaming and snorting. The voices had reached the pigs and were tormenting them in the same way they had tortured the man for years. The pigs were rushing around, crashing into rocks and biting each other as the voices sent them into a crazed and desperate rage. Unable to control themselves, they staggered closer and closer to the edge of the cliff. The staggering became a trot, the trot became a run. Trying to rid themselves of the voices, the pigs dashed off the edge of the cliff. Falling, falling, falling, they crashed into the sea, taking the voices with them.

The man walked with Jesus and his friends to the town, talking and laughing all the way. He wanted to go with Jesus wherever he went. But Jesus had another job for him to do.

'Go home,' Jesus said, 'and tell everyone how much God has done for you today.'

Note for the reader

The events depicted in Legion are based on the story recorded in Luke 8:26–39. The author has woven these stories together with historical and archeological evidence of life in first-century Judea to help you explore the difficult questions that the Bible text raises.

Read the Bible passage about Jesus and the demon-possessed man and reflect on what they tell you about God. What is God saying to you through these stories? If you have any questions, find a Christian you trust and chat through your ideas, thoughts and concerns.

What are Dark Chapters?

What is the Christian response to the vast array of horror books aimed at young people? Is it to condemn these titles and ban them from our shelves? Is it to ignore this trend and let our young people get on with reading them? At Scripture Union, we believe this presents a fantastic opportunity to help young people get into the pages of God's Word and wrestle with some of the difficult questions of faith.

The text does not sensationalise the horrific aspects of each story for entertainment's sake, and therefore trivialise what the story has to say. On the contrary, each retold account uses the more fantastic and gruesome epsiodes of each character's story to grip the reader and draw them into assessing why these events take place.

The reader is asked throughout the books to consider questions about the nature of God, how we should live as Christians, what value we place on things of this world – power, wealth, influence or popularity – and what God values.

The Dance of Death

Salome walked uncertainly, carrying her prize. Even though the eyes on the head were facing the other way, she felt as though they were looking at her, accusing her of murder. The plate was heavy – she had no idea a head could weigh this much – and the pool of congealed blood made the head glide around the plate and it threatened to slide onto the floor.

A man sits in a dungeon, plagued by doubt and fear. And his sentence is not about to end in release... but death.

Flip the book to read more about
The Dance of Death!

Babylon

Daniel is far from home. Jerusalem has been decimated and he has been taken back to Babylon, the most powerful city in the world. As he enters the gates, he feels sick with revulsion. This will be his home for the next seventy years, perhaps even more, but will he be able to stay true to Yahweh, even despite the horrific dangers that will bring?

Babylon

Hannah MacFarlane

£5.99
978 1 84427 618 9

Dark Chapters: John the Baptist

The Dance of Death

© Scripture Union 2011
First published 2011
ISBN 978 1 84427 623 3

Scripture Union
207–209 Queensway, Bletchley, Milton Keynes, MK2 2EB
Email: info@scriptureunion.org.uk
Website: www.scriptureunion.org.uk

Scripture Union Australia
Locked Bag 2, Central Coast Business Centre, NSW 2252
Website: www.scriptureunion.org.au

Scripture Union USA
PO Box 987, Valley Forge, PA 19482
Website: www.scriptureunion.org

The right of Alex Taylor to be identified as the author of this work has been
asserted by him in accordance with the Copyright, Designs and Patents Act
1988.

British Library Cataloguing-in-Publication Data
A catalogue record of this book is available from the British Library.

Printed and bound in the UK by Bell and Bain Limited, Glasgow
Cover design: GoBallistic

↳ Scripture Union is an international charity working with churches in more
than 130 countries, providing resources to bring the good news of Jesus Christ
to children, young people and families and to encourage them to develop
spiritually through the Bible and prayer.

As well as our network of volunteers, staff and associates who run holidays,
church-based events and school Christian groups, we produce a wide range
of publications

The Dance of Death

Deep in the dungeon, the scene played out in John's mind. Water was dripping continually on his head as he remembered the confrontation.

'It is not right for you to take your brother's wife.'

Herodias' face was a mixture of shock and hatred. She sat on the throne next to Herod, dressed in a long embroidered purple tunic and a gold shawl. Herod himself looked uneasy – it was difficult to know whom he was afraid of most: John the Baptist, standing before him as if he were Elijah; or Herodias, his new wife, sitting next to him looking like Jezebel. Was he really as weak as Ahab?

'How dare you!' shrieked Herodias. Then she turned her stare onto her husband.

'Are you just going to sit there while this... this monster insults me?'

John remembered how he had stood, his eyes boring into Herod, ignoring Herodias' outrage.

'It is not right for you to take your brother's wife.'

That had been months ago. John knew he had been doing the Lord's work when he went before the king, but during the seemingly endless time in the dark, damp royal dungeons, he had begun to doubt. It was hard to keep going when he couldn't go to the synagogue or talk to the priests or any of God's people, apart from a few of his followers.

As he had left the court that day, soldiers had grabbed him by the arms and legs and carried him roughly back into the palace. But instead of going back to the throne room, he had been taken down. Down into the depths of the great building, to a place where there was no window, no light, no hope. He had realised straight away that Herod had given in to his wife's demands and had him arrested. He was not like Elijah after all. He could not run or disappear as God's great prophet had done. He was trapped in the darkness.

A month or so ago, John had heard more about the actions of his cousin, Jesus. Immediately he had sent a few of his followers to ask him if he really was the One. Jesus had sent a message that had fired John's heart for a time. The blind were seeing! The dead were being raised to life! Jesus had even confirmed that John was the new Elijah! When he heard this, John recalled the events of his birth. His conception had been announced by an angel who told his father that John would lead

many people to turn back to God and that he would have the same power and spirit as Elijah.

But the passing days had worn John down. He knew that Herod would only stand up to his wife's nagging for so long. His end would come soon, if he wasn't released. And so, here he was. Not for him the fiery chariots and whirlwinds of Elijah's ascent to heaven. Just the dark, the rats and the smell of excrement.

Way above, in the royal dining room, a celebration was taking place. It was Herod's birthday and he was throwing a lavish party. All the great and good of Galilee were there – officials, army officers, leaders – this was going to be a party that no one would forget! Around the edges of the hall, Herodias hurried and directed, ordered and organised. She wanted this to be the best party her husband had ever had. He had spent far too long worrying about that troublemaker in the dungeons below. She had to do two things: take his mind off John, and find the best way to get rid of the baptiser.

When all the guests were reclining in their places, servants started to bring in the food: great platters of lamb and chicken, fish from the lake, huge baskets of bread, fruit and sweetcakes… the food kept coming and coming. Herod smiled to himself.

'Wine!' he shouted, raising his goblet in the air. 'We must all have wine!'

The army officers cheered as the servants came round with large jugs of a particularly fine vintage.

All around, hands reached for the food. The conversation was boisterous and as the wine flowed it became more and more vulgar. The king chatted loudly to his general and his chief adviser. Further down the room, the junior officers cracked jokes about the latest scandal involving an official in the Roman governor's household who had been caught stealing dormice from the governor's kitchen. Every few seconds the place erupted with laughter as a punchline was delivered.

As time wore on, the party slowed. The officers were by now very drunk and the officials were looking around them uncomfortably, worried that a fight might break out at any moment. Herodias, concerned that her party might descend into an all-out brawl, caught sight of her daughter out of the corner of her eye.

'Salome! Get over here!'

'Yes, mother?'

'Go in there and dance, before that terrible Captain Titus starts insulting the Emperor.'

'In there? I can't! They'll go mad! They've drunk almost all the wine we have in the palace!'

'Salome, shut up and get in there!'

Herodias pushed her daughter into the hall. When the guests saw her arrive, a great cheer went up around

the tables. Salome looked uncertain and looked back at her mother.

'Dance!' cried one officer.

'Yes, dance!' shouted two more.

Suddenly, a chant struck up around the hall: 'Dance! Dance! Dance! Dance! Dance!'

The musicians, who had been playing throughout the meal, struck up a seductive tune and Salome started to move nervously to the music. The guests cheered.

'Yeeeeeees!'

'Wa-hey!'

'Dance! Dance! Dance!'

The cheers continued and the music got faster. Salome danced and danced. The faster the music went, the faster she danced. The crowd clapped, the crowd whistled. Salome writhed and gyrated, she tapped and she span, she twirled and she cavorted. The eyes of every man in the room were fixed on her; some even dropped their cups, and wine spilt all over the floor.

By the time the music died down, all the men were on their feet. Herod clapped his hands and laughed, wine dribbling down his chin. Some of the younger officers, their discipline eroded by the wine and the charged atmosphere, made to grab Salome. Exhausted as she was, she forced herself to run to the edge of the hall and her mother's waiting arms. The most avid of her pursuers made a last-ditch attempt to catch her but

instead lunged into the gilt edge of a table. His forehead cracked against the furniture and he collapsed onto the floor. The hall was silenced as junior officers flicked their eyes anxiously from their bleeding comrade to the king and back again.

The king stared at the growing pool of blood at the end of the room. Then he threw back his head and roared with laughter. The tension broke immediately and servants rushed to help the stricken soldier.

'Salome! Salome! Come back in here!' cried the king.

Applause rang in Salome's ears as she approached her stepfather nervously and bowed before him.

'Yes, my Lord.'

'That was sensational! Your mother has obviously taught you well. This is the one of the best birthdays I have ever celebrated and, as the men here like you so much that they are falling over themselves to meet you—'

Sniggering from the lower ranks interrupted the king, but was silenced by a sharp look from the senior captain.

'As I was saying, as you have danced so beautifully, you may ask me for anything and it will be yours. I will give you as much as half my kingdom, if you want it!'

Gasps echoed through the hall as the size of the gift sunk in, then applause broke out. Salome looked uncertain. She had seen her stepfather drunk before, but he had never made such a promise. She had no idea

what to ask for. Looking round for help, she saw only the leering faces of her father's dinner guests. She retreated nervously back towards the door and her mother.

When she got there, she asked her mother what she should do.

Herodias realised that this was her chance. Now John would pay for treating her like a modern-day Jezebel. She whispered in Salome's ear.

'I want the head of John the Baptist. Now. On a dish.'

The king's jaw dropped open. His stepdaughter could not have just said that.

'W-w-w-what? Are you sure?'

Salome nodded her head. 'Yes.'

The king didn't know what to do. His drunken promise had suddenly turned against him. He didn't like some of the things John said, but he didn't want to kill him. After all, he'd only had John arrested to please Herodias.

Herodias.

He could see his wife standing in the doorway. He realised she had been the one who had told Salome what to say. But he couldn't go back on his word. He couldn't refuse, not in front of his guests.

John looked up as he heard footsteps approaching. Light from a flaming torch was coming closer and closer. The

bolt was slid back and the door opened. Hands grabbed his shoulders and he was dragged out of the cell.

'Where are you taking me?' John gasped.

There was no reply.

'Where… are… you… tak—'

A punch to the mouth stopped John from saying any more. Suddenly John knew what was going to happen. This was it. There was no escape.

As the guards continued wordlessly, John sagged in their arms. His head hurt and he could hardly breathe. His mind drifted back to the River Jordan. He had spent many days there, baptising people, telling them to turn back to God. He thought of one particular morning, one glorious morning when he had come. Jesus. The Messiah. The one who was going to save the world. And it had been John's privilege to baptise Jesus. As Jesus had come out of the water, a dove came down from heaven. And God had spoken to Jesus. He spoke for all to hear.

'You are my own dear Son, and I am pleased with you.'

John prayed to that same God now.

'Lord, what will happen to me? Was I wrong to speak to the king like that? Did I get it all wrong?'

Then the Lord spoke. Not in a loud voice for everyone to hear, but in a whisper, just as he had spoken to Elijah all those years before.

'No, my good and faithful servant. You did what I asked, and now you are coming home.'

The guards arrived in the courtyard with their prisoner, his eyes screwed up against the light. Unthinking, they threw him on the ground and forced him to bow his head. Blood from a previous execution was still splattered across the floor and it smeared across the prisoner's knees as he was manoeuvred into position. The guards didn't care.

One of the guards picked up a sword and measured it against the prisoner's neck. The other picked up the plate that Herodias had provided.

The guard swung the sword high above his head and brought it down on the prisoner. The blade sliced easily through the neck and throat, as if it were cutting through a piece of fruit. As soon as the blade passed through, the head fell onto the floor and blood sprayed over the courtyard. The body collapsed and a red stain spread across the sand floor, as if the body were trying to make a copy of the head that had just been taken from it.

The guard put down the sword and wiped the prisoner's blood from his uniform. He picked up the head by the hair to put it on the plate. As he did so, the mouth dropped open and spewed out more blood. The guards staggered back to avoid getting more gore on

their clothes. Suddenly a gust of wind rushed through the courtyard and caught the prisoner's voice box. A gravelly moan issued from the open mouth and echoed round the walls.

Both men looked at each other, frozen in terror. Then the guard who was holding the head snapped out of his shock and threw it onto the plate, sending the face skittering into his companion's chest. Blood from the prisoner's eyes oozed down his breastplate and, around the base of the head, a thick, gelatinous pool spread over the plate.

Salome walked uncertainly, carrying her prize. Even though the eyes on the head were facing the other way, she felt as though they were looking at her, accusing her of murder. The plate was heavy – she had no idea a head could weigh this much – and the pool of congealed blood made the head glide around the plate and it threatened to slide onto the floor. The soldiers at the entrance to the king's great hall opened the doors and let her in. One of them grimaced as the girl went past with her trophy. Inside, the party had dissipated and only the king and queen remained.

Salome walked up to the thrones to present the head to her mother. As she approached, she saw a peculiar expression on her mother's face. Was it triumph? Excitement? But her stepfather was a white as a sheet,

and his face displayed a horror that was beyond description.

'Thank you for my prize, my Lord,' Salome bowed as far as she could while still holding the head.

Herodias smiled, but Herod could only stammer, 'T-t-take it aw-away!'

'Oh no!' said Herodias, smiling. 'We must appreciate such a generous gift. My child, place it here on this table next to the king, so that everyone may see what happens to someone who challenges the great Herod Antipas!'

Salome went to place the head on the table so that the face would look out at anyone approaching the throne. However, as she put the plate down, her hand slipped and it crashed onto the table. Salome watched as the head slid from the plate and, almost in slow motion, rolled into Herod's lap.

The smile vanished completely from Herodias' face. Herod, unable to move, opened his mouth in a silent scream.

The dead eyes of John the Baptist stared up at the man who had ordered his execution.

Note for the reader

The events depicted in The Dance of Death are based on the stories recorded in Matthew 11:1–19 and 14:1–12. The author has woven these stories together with historical and archeological evidence of life in first-century Judea to help you explore the difficult questions that the Bible text raises.

Read the Bible passages about John the Baptist, Herod and Jesus, and reflect on what they tell you about God. What is God saying to you through these stories? If you have any questions, find a Christian you trust and chat through your ideas, thoughts and concerns.

What are Dark Chapters?

What is the Christian response to the vast array of horror books aimed at young people? Is it to condemn these titles and ban them from our shelves? Is it to ignore this trend and let our young people get on with reading them? At Scripture Union, we believe this presents a fantastic opportunity to help young people get into the pages of God's Word and wrestle with some of the difficult questions of faith.

The text does not sensationalise the horrific aspects of each story for entertainment's sake, and therefore trivialise what the story has to say. On the contrary, each retold account uses the more fantastic and gruesome epsiodes of each character's story to grip the reader and draw them into assessing why these events take place.

The reader is asked throughout the books to consider questions about the nature of God, how we should live as Christians, what value we place on things of this world – power, wealth, influence or popularity – and what God values.

Legion

He couldn't remember when they had first come to him, it felt like they had always been there, and he knew it wouldn't be long before they started to scream at him again. When that happened he would do anything to try and escape them – he would hit his head, smash his fists against rocks, tear his hair out, anything. Anything to get rid of the voices.

A man rages on a hillside, driven mad by the voices in his head. And the voices aren't leaving without a fight...

Flip the book to read more about Legion!

The Oncoming Storm

Noah has been called by the Holy One, called to build an ark to escape the Holy One's judgement on the people of the earth. But Noah is the only person still faithful to the Holy One – who will believe that destruction is coming? They are too busy worshipping their own gods to listen to Noah – the Holy One will stand their faithlessness no longer. The storm is coming…

The Oncoming Storm

Andrew R Guyatt

£5.99
978 1 84427 619 6

The Sky will Fall

Shimsom thought back over all he had achieved for the Lord. He was one of God's judges, appointed by the Lord to guide his people and rid them of Philistine rule. But Shimsom's methods – a donkey's jawbone, pairs of foxes, a Philistine marriage – had led him here, tied to pillars in the Temple of Dagon. But if he was going to meet a gruesome end, then he would take everyone else with him…

The Sky Will Fall

Darren R Hill

£5.99
978 1 84427 537 3

The Egyptian Nightmare

Pharaoh is ruler of all he surveys. His kingdom is prosperous and his monuments are being built at a fantastic rate by his Hebrew slaves. But suddenly, Moses and Aaron appear in his palace and demand the release of the God's people. As events spiral out of his control and God strikes his country with terrifying plagues, Pharaoh's desperate attempts to regain power only lead to his own destruction.

The Egyptian Nightmare

Hannah MacFarlane

£5.99
978 1 84427 535 9

Izevel, Queen of Darkness

Slowly, slowly, slowly, Izevel Princess of Tyre, works her influence over her new husband, Ahav, and his kingdom Israel. Leading them away from Adonai, she encourages the unspeakable practices of Baal worship. But despite her best efforts, the Lord and his prophets will not be disposed of so easily. Increasingly driven mad by her own lifestyle, Izevel races headlong towards her own grisly downfall.

Izevel,
Queen of Darkness

Kate Chamberlayne

£5.99
978 1 84427 536 6